BRAIN ACADEMY
MATHS

MISSION FILE 3

Charlotte Haggis,
Louise Moore and
Richard Cooper

Consultants for NACE:
Elaine Sellars and
Sue Lowndes

n·a·c·e

RISING STARS

Rising Stars are grateful to the following people for their support in developing this series: Sue Mordecai, Julie Fitzpatrick, Johanna Raffan and Belle Wallace.

NACE, PO Box 242, Arnolds Way, Oxford, OX2 9FR
www.nace.co.uk

Rising Stars Ltd, 22 Grafton Street, London, W1S 4EX
www.risingstars-uk.com

Every effort has been made to trace copyright holders and obtain their permission for the use of copyright materials. The authors and publisher will gladly receive information enabling them to rectify any error or omission in subsequent editions.

All facts are correct at time of going to press.

Published 2004
Reprinted 2005, 2006, 2008, 2009
Text, design and layout © Rising Stars UK Ltd.
TASC: Thinking Actively in a Social Context © Belle Wallace 2004

Editorial: Charlotte Haggis, Louise Moore and Richard Cooper
Editorial Consultants: Elaine Sellars, Sue Lowndes and Sally Harbour
Design: Burville-Riley
Illustrations: Cover and insides – Sue Lee / Characters – Bill Greenhead
Cover design: Burville-Riley

British Library Cataloguing in Publication Data.
A CIP record for this book is available from the British Library.

ISBN: 978-1-904591-37-5

Printed by Craft Print International Limited, Singapore

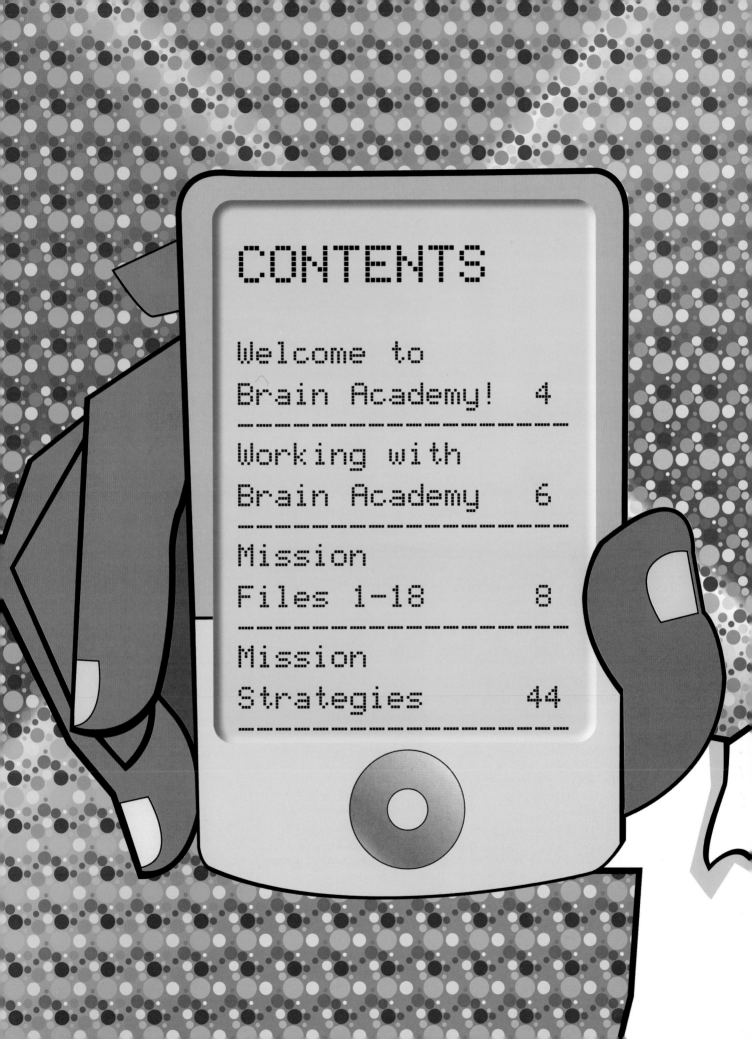

CONTENTS

Welcome to
Brain Academy!   4

Working with
Brain Academy   6

Mission
Files 1-18   8

Mission
Strategies   44

Welcome to Brain Academy!

Welcome to Brain Academy! Make yourself at home. We are here to give you the low-down on the organisation – so pay attention!

It's our job to help Da Vinci and his colleagues to solve the tough problems they face and we would like you to join us as members of the Academy. Are you up to the challenge?

Da Vinci

Da Vinci is the founder and head of the Brain Academy. He is all seeing, all thinking and all knowing – possibly the cleverest person alive. Nobody has ever actually seen him in the flesh as he communicates only via computer. When Da Vinci receives an emergency call for help, the members of Brain Academy jump into action (and that means you!).

Huxley

Huxley is Da Vinci's right-hand man. Not as clever, but still very smart. He is here to guide you through the missions and offer help and advice. The sensible and reliable face of Brain Academy, Huxley is cool under pressure.

Dr Hood

The mad doctor is the arch-enemy of Da Vinci and Brain Academy. He has set up a rival organisation called D.A.F.T. (which stands for Dull And Feeble Thinkers). Dr Hood and his agents will do anything they can to irritate and annoy the good people of this planet. He is a pain we could do without.

Hilary Kumar

Ms Kumar is the Prime Minister of our country. As the national leader she has a hotline through to the Academy but will only call in an extreme emergency. Confident and strong willed, she is a very tough cookie indeed.

General Cods-Wallop

This highly decorated gentleman (with medals, not wallpaper) is in charge of the armed forces. Most of his success has come from the help of Da Vinci and the Academy rather than the use of his somewhat limited military brain.

Mrs Tiggles

Stella Tiggles is the retired head of the Secret Intelligence service. She is a particular favourite of Da Vinci who treats her as his own mother. Mrs Tiggles' faithful companion is her cat Bond... James Bond.

We were just like you once – ordinary schoolchildren leading ordinary lives. Then one day we all received a call from a strange character named Da Vinci. From that day on, we have led a double life – as secret members of Brain Academy!

Here are a few things you should know about the people you'll meet on your journey.

Maryland T. Wordsworth

M.T. Wordsworth is the president of the USA. Not the sharpest tool in the box, Maryland prefers to be known by his middle name, Texas, or 'Tex' for short. He takes great exception to being referred to as 'Mary' (which has happened in the past).

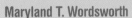

Buster Crimes

Buster is a really smooth dude and is in charge of the Police Force. His laid-back but efficient style has won him many friends, although these don't include Dr Hood or the agents of D.A.F.T. who regularly try to trick the coolest cop in town.

Sandy Buckett

The fearless Sandy Buckett is the head of the fire service. Sandy and her team of brave firefighters are always on hand, whether to extinguish the flames of chaos caused by the demented Dr Hood or just to rescue Mrs Tiggles' cat…

Echo the Eco-Warrior

Echo is the hippest chick around. Her love of nature and desire for justice will see her do anything to help an environmental cause – even if it means she's going to get her clothes dirty.

Victor Blastov

Victor Blastov is the leading scientist at the Space Agency. He once tried to build a rocket by himself but failed to get the lid off the glue. Victor often requires the services of the Academy, even if it's to set the video to record Dr Who.

Prince Barrington

Prince Barrington, or 'Bazza' as he is known to his friends, is the publicity-seeking heir to the throne. Always game for a laugh, the Prince will stop at nothing to raise money for worthy causes. A 'good egg' as his mother might say.

Working with Brain Academy

Do you get the idea? Now you've had the introduction we are going to show you the best way to use this book.

The plot

This tells you what the mission is about.

MISSION FILE 3:5

Prince Barrington gets shirty

Time: Early Morning
Place: Arsenic F.C.

After a string of terrible performances, Five-A-Side football team Arsenic F.C. are set to be relegated from the 'Starling Premiership'. Their Manager, Peckham Beckham has asked Prince Barrington to help his team avoid the drop and save him from getting the boot!

Da Vinci, this is a horrible task! Where do I start?

You need to begin by sharing some tactics in the dressing room. Hopefully we'll see some changes!

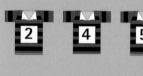

The Training Mission

Huxley will give you some practice before sending you on the main mission.

The Prince feels that the run of poor performances is because of the order the team run onto the pitch.

2 **4** **5**

1) How many different ways are there that Prince Barrington can arrange the THREE players in an orderly line?

2) Player number three joins the team. How many different ways could the Prince arrange the FOUR players?

16

Each mission is divided up into different parts.

No one said this was easy. In fact that is why you have been chosen. Da Vinci will only take the best and he believes that includes you. Good luck!

Each book contains a number of 'missions' for you to take part in. You will work with the characters in Brain Academy to complete these missions.

The Main Mission

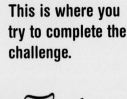

This is where you try to complete the challenge.

M1

The Prince believes that when the players run out on to the pitch in this order, they will be certain to win the match. Can you help to organise the team?

2 **4** **5** **10** **15**

1) Arrange the differently numbered players in a line so that:
The total of the numbers on the first THREE shirts is 11.
The total of the numbers on the last THREE shirts is 27.
The first shirt is half the value of the last shirt.

4 **4** **5** **5** **10** **10**

2) THREE members of each squad line up for a photograph. Organise the players to stand in a line so that:
Between the TWO number four shirts there are TWO other players.
Between the TWO number ten shirts there are THREE other players.
Between the TWO number five shirts there is ONE other player.

The Da Vinci Files

These problems are for the best Brain Academy recruits. Very tough. Are you tough enough?

Fantastic! So far Arsenic F.C. are unbeaten. If Barrington can take the Da Vinci Challenge the nation will get to hear of the team's success and Peckham Beckham's job will be saved.

Da Vinci Files

A photographer wants to take a photo of the red team in M1. There must be a shirt with an even number at each end of the line. Find all the possible combinations the team could stand in.

Huxley's Think Tank

Try using counters or cards with the numbers on to try different arrangements of numbers.

17

Huxley's Think Tank

Huxley will download some useful tips onto your PDA to help you on each mission.

PS: See pages 44–47 for a useful process and hints and tips!

D.A.F.T. agents get the boot!

Time: Early morning
Place: Hilary Kumar's office

Hilary Kumar has agreed to help some frantic farmers. There is only a week to go before the National Farming Championships and a gang of D.A.F.T. agents have decided to disrupt the farmers preparations by stealing all their wellies. This is a job for Brain Academy.

> Da Vinci, can we help?

> Completing Huxley's Training Mission will help you recover those wellingtons!

TM

> Right then Hilary, if we can work out how many pairs have been pinched we can get back those boots.

1) Apple Farm lost the same number of pairs of boots as Plum Farm. Cherry Farm lost twice as many pairs as Plum Farm. Peach Farm lost the same number of pairs as Cherry Farm. If they lost a total of 24 pairs of boots, how many were stolen from each farm?

2) If they lost a total of 42 pairs of boots, how many were stolen from each farm?

1) FOUR D.A.F.T. agents stole a total of 17 pairs of boots.

Dick has ONE more pair than Rick.
Rick took TWICE as many pairs as Mick.
Mick stole FOUR pairs less than Nick.
Dick, Mick and Nick took a total of THIRTEEN pairs of boots.

How many pairs did each D.A.F.T. agent take?

2) FIVE D.A.F.T. agents stole a total of TWENTY pairs of boots.

Nick has THREE less pairs than Rick.
Rick stole ONE more pair than Mick.
Vic took TWO more pairs than Mick.
Dick has HALF as many pairs as Vic.

How many pairs did each D.A.F.T. agent take?

Great stuff, Hilary! If we can work out how many wellies each agent stole, we'll have this stinky crime solved in no time!

'Boot'iful work! Completing the Da Vinci Challenge will ensure the boots are returned and the Farmers can take part in the National Farming Championships.

Da Vinci files

The police return 24 pairs of boots to the farms. Plum gets half the pairs of boots. Apple gets half the remainder. Then Peach has two thirds of what's left and the rest go to Cherry. How many pairs of boots did each farm get?

Huxley's Think Tank

Try to find one fact that you know and then work systematically through the rest. Use cubes to help you.

9

What a load of rubbish!

Time: Early morning
Place: The town of Dumpton

Echo the Eco-Warrior has just heard that the dustmen of Dumpton have all been sacked and the streets are now covered in rubbish. This terrible news has caused her to worry herself sick (and she was green enough to start with). Can you help Echo clean up and return Dumpton to its former glory?

What on earth should I do, Da Vinci?

Before you can start clearing those streets you need to take the Training Mission.

TM

Echo will need the help of a friend. Let's see how much rubbish they can both pick up in two minutes.

1) When Echo counted the pieces she found that the total was a TWO-digit number that is a square number and a multiple of 12. How many items of rubbish did she collect?

2) Echo's pal, Summer counted her pieces of rubbish in 7s. She got more than Echo, but less than a hundred. Echo counted Summer's rubbish in 12s – she got an exact answer. How much rubbish has Summer collected?

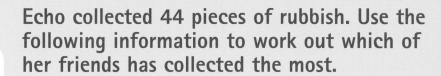

Echo collected 44 pieces of rubbish. Use the following information to work out which of her friends has collected the most.

Echo and Summer take their friend, Forest, over to Dumpton to help clean up the streets. The three friends decide to have a competition to see who can collect the most litter.

1) Summer had between 40 and 70 pieces of rubbish.
   When she counted her pieces of rubbish in 7s there were THREE pieces left over.
   When she counted her pieces of rubbish in 4s there were TWO pieces left over.

   How much rubbish did she collect?

2) Forest had between 40 and 70 pieces of rubbish.
   When he counted his pieces of rubbish in 4s there were TWO pieces left over.
   When he counted his pieces of rubbish in 5s there were THREE pieces left over.

   How much rubbish did he collect?

What a successful mission! Echo and her pals are on a roll. They will love this Da Vinci Challenge.

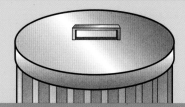

Da Vinci files

The gang collect the same amount of rubbish as they did in M1 each day.

1) If they start on a Monday, on which day will they collect their 1000th piece?

2) How many pieces will they have collected by the end of that day?

Huxley's Think Tank

Huxley says think in multiples... and don't forget about those remainders!

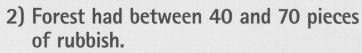

Hats off to Prince Barrington!

Time: Mid-afternoon
Place: Prince Bazza's mansion

There's a hair-ific problem in the town of Little Follicle. Lockdrop, a terrible disease, is causing people's hair to drop out. Prince Barrington decides that as doctors can't get to the root of the problem, he'll lend a helping hand.

I don't want anyone to dye, Da Vinci! What should I do?

Huxley has a Training Mission that will make your hair stand on end!

Before we can help these people we need to know how many families in the village have caught Lockdrop.

All the families in Green Street have caught Lockdrop. Only families of THREE and families of FOUR people live in this street. 24 people have caught the disease.

1) How many families of THREE and FOUR could there be?

All the families in Baker Street have caught Lockdrop. Only families of THREE and families of FIVE people live in this street. 42 people have caught the disease.

2) How many families of THREE and FIVE could there be?
Find all the possibilities.

The Prince has asked a local knitting club to make several hundred woolly bobble hats. The hats will be used to stop the patients catching a cold while they wait for treatment.

When the first batch of hats was ready the Prince took them to the Post Office.

Each stamp costs either 8p or 7p.

1) If the parcel cost 52p to post, and Bazza sticks on SEVEN stamps, how many of each stamp did Bazza stick on the parcel?

2) What if the parcel cost 83p? How many stamps could he stick on?

Superb! If only the Prince could solve the Da Vinci Challenge then this terrible disease will be cured forever!

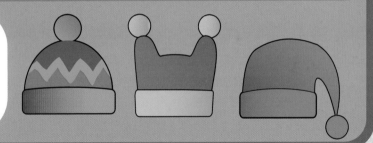

Da Vinci files

When the second lot of hats was taken to the post office Bazza was told it would cost 72p to post. Bazza stuck on some stamps. This time each stamp cost 8p, 7p or 5p.

Find all the possible combinations of stamps that the Prince could put on his parcel.

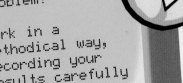

Huxley's Think Tank

Don't forget those tables! They'll be helpful when solving this problem!

Work in a methodical way, recording your results carefully as you go.

Flying high!

Time: Early evening
Place: British Army headquarters

General Cods-Wallop is in a sorry state as he thinks his Army's flag is dull and boring. He is getting himself in quite a flap over this problem! Mrs Tiggles has agreed to help.

The General will be flying high if I can design a flag. Where do I begin, Da Vinci?

Huxley's Training Mission will get you started!

TM

The General is no square himself, so Mrs Tiggles designs a flag made of rectangles.

How many rectangles can you count in Mrs Tiggles' design?

Some flags with triangles will certainly help to perk the General up! Can you help Mrs Tiggles count the triangles in these flags?

1)

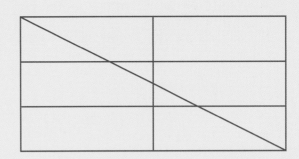

2)

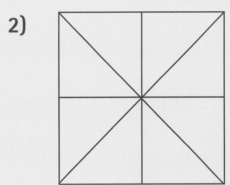

If Mrs Tiggles can take the Da Vinci Challenge the General will soon be flying his flag with pride!

Da Vinci files

How many rectangles can you count in this design?

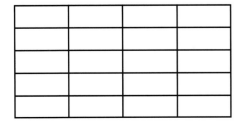

Huxley's Think Tank

Don't forget overlapping shapes!

Prince Barrington gets shirty

Time: Early Morning
Place: Arsenic F.C.

After a string of terrible performances, Five-A-Side football team Arsenic F.C. are set to be relegated from the 'Starling Premiership'. Their Manager, Peckham Beckham has asked Prince Barrington to help his team avoid the drop and save him from getting the boot!

5-0

Da Vinci, this is a horrible task! Where do I start?

You need to begin by sharing some tactics in the dressing room. Hopefully we'll see some changes!

The Prince feels that the run of poor performances is because of the order the team run onto the pitch.

2   4   5

1) How many different ways are there that Prince Barrington can arrange the THREE players in an orderly line?

2) Player number three joins the team. How many different ways could the Prince arrange the FOUR players?

1) Arrange the differently numbered players in a line so that:
The total of the numbers on the first THREE shirts is 11.
The total of the numbers on the last THREE shirts is 27.
The first shirt is half the value of the last shirt.

The Prince believes that when the players run out on to the pitch in this order, they will be certain to win the match. Can you help to organise the team?

2) THREE members of each squad line up for a photograph. Organise the players to stand in a line so that:
Between the TWO number four shirts there are TWO other players.
Between the TWO number ten shirts there are THREE other players.
Between the TWO number five shirts there is ONE other player.

Fantastic! So far Arsenic F.C. are unbeaten. If Barrington can take the Da Vinci Challenge the nation will get to hear of the team's success and Peckham Beckham's job will be saved.

Da Vinci Files

A photographer wants to take a photo of the red team in M1. There must be a shirt with an even number at each end of the line. Find all the possible combinations the team could stand in.

Huxley's Think Tank

Try using counters or cards with the numbers on to try different arrangements of numbers.

what a cat-astrophe!

Time: Lunchtime
Place: Mrs Tiggle's house

Sandy Buckett has agreed to help Mrs Stella Tiggles. James Bond, her beloved feline friend has eaten one too many of his favourite 'Cat Snacks' and can no longer fit through the cat flap. Sandy needs to call Brain Academy!

What a cat-astrophe, Da Vinci! What shall I do?

Huxley has a 'purrfect' Training Mission for you Sandy!

Firstly, we must help Stella by changing the diet of her podgy pussy cat! Pop down to 'Pet Kingdom' and buy some healthy cat food!

'Trim Tuna' is HALF the price of skimmed milk

Skimmed milk is £1.00 more than 'Fat Free Frisks'

'Low Fat Treats' are TWICE the price of 'Fat Free Frisks'

'Low Fat Treats' cost £4.00 more than 'Trim Tuna'

1) Sandy bought one of each item and spent £15.00. How much did each item cost?

2) If the total bill is £24.00 but 'Low Fat Treats' cost £7.00 more than 'Trim Tuna', how much would each item cost?

The cats are weighed in pairs. Each cat weighs a complete number of kilos.

FIRST SET OF SCALES

1) James and Splodge weigh 5kg altogether.
Splodge and Bouncer weigh 7kg altogether.
Bouncer and Tigger weigh 11kg altogether.
Tigger and James weigh 9kg altogether.

How much could each cat weigh?

SECOND SET OF SCALES

2) James and Splodge weigh 10kg altogether.
Splodge and Bouncer weigh 9kg altogether.
Bouncer and Tigger weigh 12 kg altogether.
Tigger and James weigh 13kg altogether.

How much could each cat weigh?

Find as many solutions as you can.

Sandy must weigh James and his friends to help solve the problem. She uses two sets of scales.

If Sandy can take the Da Vinci Challenge she'll be able to help James squeeze back through his cat flap!

Da Vinci files

At the end of the first week James and Splodge weighed a total of 7kg on the second set if scales.
James and Tigger weighed a total of 10kg.
All the other total weights stayed the same.
What could the new weights of the cats be?
Find all the possibilities.

Huxley's Think Tank

Huxley says don't give up on this. Keep trying different combinations of numbers and you'll soon hit the purrrfect weight!

Testing times for Year 6 thieves!

Time: Late afternoon
Place: The Police Station

Police Commissioner Crimes has arrested FOUR D.A.F.T. agents who were caught stealing the answers to this year's Maths SATs questions. The FOUR agents have code names making this a hard crime to crack! Can you help Buster solve this calculated crime?

I need to find the answer to this problem, Da Vinci! What shall I do?

Huxley has a Training Mission for you. Get SATs down and we can begin!

After questioning the FOUR agents, Buster found that they each have an undercover codename. R U Sure, B A Swot, I M Clever and I C Answers.

I M Clever planned the robbery with Andy and Maggie. Sally distracted the security men with R U Sure and I M Clever.
R U Sure, B A Swot and Andy broke into the building.
R U Sure and Dave nearly got away.

Can you help Buster work out who is who?

A police informer later revealed the surnames of the appalling agents as Green, Black, Brown and White. After more confused questioning Crimes found out the following information.

White's fingerprints were found on the door with B A Swot and Maggie's.

Sally has committed a crime before with Brown and Green.

Green, Andy and R U Sure are all facing a long stretch in prison.

Can you help him further by finding the surname of each offender?

These D.A.F.T. agents have certainly put Crimes to the test. He'll be able to convict them as soon as he has completed the Da Vinci Challenge.

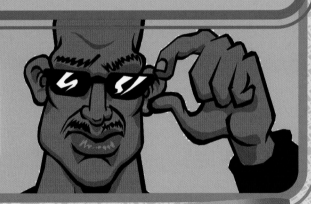

Da Vinci files

There were EIGHT exam papers which were numbered ONE to EIGHT. I C Answers stole THREE exam papers.
If the numbers on these papers add up to 15, which papers did he steal?

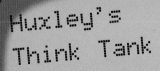

Huxley's Think Tank

Huxley says it's all a process of elimination!

Tourist troubles for Tex

Time: Mid-morning
Place: Paris

The President of France, Frank French has a terrible problem. The Trifle Tower has collapsed! Hundreds of angry tourists are rioting because they can't take a trip to the top of the tower. President Maryland T Wordsworth of the United States has agreed to help his friend by sending the tourists to some other equally famous landmarks.

PARIS

Bonjour, Da Vinci. Will you help me... S'il vous plaît?

Huxley's Training Mission should help to ease those tourists' tempers!

President Maryland T Wordsworth has paid for 96 tourists to travel on some open top buses. He needs some help in dividing the tourists equally between the buses.

Sunny Tours

1) How can they be divided equally between
a) FOUR buses
b) SIX buses
c) EIGHT buses
if each group of buses seats the same number of people?

2) If each bus holds a maximum of 18 people, how many buses will he need? How many spare seats, if any, will there be?

Tex has decided to hire a ferry and a rowing boat to take the tourists on a cruise up the River Seine, but he needs some help getting them on board.

At first, 18 tourists climb into the rowing boat and 31 pile into the ferry. The President decides to rearrange the tourists so that there are THREE more tourists in the ferry than the rowing boat.

1) How many tourists must move from the ferry to the rowing boat?

Tex finds an inflatable dinghy. The tourists are rearranged and there are now the same amount of people in the rowing boat and the ferry. The inflatable dinghy has ONE more tourist on board than the ferry.

2) How many people in the dinghy?

3) How many people left the ferry and the rowing boat?

Bravo! If Tex can solve the Da Vinci Challenge, those tourists will be happy for the rest of their holiday!

Da Vinci files

30 tourists climb into the THREE boats.
There is a different, even number of people in each boat.
How many people in each boat?
Find all the possibilities.

Huxley's Think Tank

Using known tables facts and doubling them will help you with some questions.
Cubes and counters will help you with others.

Victor's in a 'hole' lot of trouble!

Time: Past bedtime
Place: NASA headquarters

Victor Blastov is so angry he's seeing stars! He has just discovered that TWO D.A.F.T. agents are trying to tunnel under NASA Headquarters in order to steal the plans for his spaceship. Buster Crimes has agreed to help NASA by catching the agents.

These men deserve a 'hole' life sentence, Da Vinci! Where should I start?

Huxley has a Training Mission that will put you in the right orbit!

Working out the answers to these questions will allow you to find those villains!

1) In FOUR days Doug Ahole and Ivor Spade dug a total of 20 metres. Each day they dug TWO metres less than the day before. How far did they dig each day?

2) In FOUR days Doug Ahole and Ivor Spade dug a total of 32 metres. Each day they dug FOUR metres less than the day before. How far did they dig each day?

3) In FIVE days Doug Ahole and Ivor Spade dug a total of 35 metres. Each day they dug THREE metres more than the day before. How far did they dig each day?

Buster will need to keep the buckets of mud and with such hard evidence they'll never dig their way out of this one! Answering these questions will help Buster work out how many buckets he'll need to put in his police car.

1) After FOUR days of digging Doug and Ivor filled a total of 48 buckets.
Each day they filled FOUR less buckets than the day before.
If they kept on filling FOUR less buckets each day, how many would they fill altogether?

After SIX days of digging they filled a total of 81 buckets with mud.
Each day they filled THREE buckets less than the day before.

2) How many buckets did Doug and Ivor fill each day?

3) If they carried on filling THREE buckets less than the day before, how many buckets would they have filled altogether?

Great work! If Crimes can solve the Da Vinci Challenge he'll convict those D.A.F.T. agents and save Victor's plans.

Da Vinci files

On Day 1 Doug fills 28 buckets. On each day afterwards he fills FOUR less.

On Day 1 Ivor fills 35 buckets. On each day afterwards he fills SEVEN less.

1) Who fills more buckets?

2) How many more?

Huxley's Think Tank

Perhaps think about digging 45 metres in 5 days like this:
_+_+_+_+_ = 45 m

It's a hat trick!

Time: Party time
Place: Prince Bazza's mansion

A group of D.A.F.T. agents are planning to gatecrash Prince Barrington's fancy dress birthday party. Sandy Buckett would like to lend the Prince three of her biggest, toughest firemen to keep them out. They are going to need the help of Brain Academy if they want to see off those agents!

What do we need to do, Da Vinci?

You'll need to begin with the Training Mission that Huxley has designed for you.

Ok, Sandy. The THREE firemen are ready, but I need you to organise some hats for them to wear.

1) Each fireman takes a hat. They each take either a helmet or a bobble hat. How many different combinations are there?

2) If each fireman takes either a helmet, a bobble hat or a cap, how many different combinations are there?

The firemen are in place but if they are going to deter those D.A.F.T. agents they'll need to be armed. Sandy gives each fireman a water pistol.

1) If FOUR firemen are each given either a red or a blue water pistol, how many possible orders are there that they can stand in?

2) If TWO firemen each choose a water pistol from a bag containing red, yellow, green, blue, purple and orange water pistols, how many possible orders are there that they can stand in?

If Sandy can take the Da Vinci Challenge she'll be sure to guarantee that birthday boy Bazza has a day to remember!

Da Vinci files

THREE firemen are given a choice of either a red or blue water pistol AND either a helmet or a bobble hat. They must each take a hat and a water pistol. List all the possible combinations.

Huxley's Think Tank

FOR THIS QUESTION YOU CAN ASSUME THE FIREMEN ARE IDENTICAL!

Rubbish engine-eering!

Time: The rush hour
Place: Snail Rail headquarters

A runaway train is currently thundering down the railway track, and it seems to be completely unstoppable! Charlie Chugalong, head of Snail Rail and old friend of Victor Blastov, had been busy building the 'Essex Express' for years. Victor has agreed to help stop the train and save the lives of hundreds of people.

How do I save this engine-eering disaster, Da Vinci?

Huxley's Training Mission will get you on the right track!

TM

First of all we need to work out how many people are on that train.

1) There are THREE carriages holding a total of 11 people. Carriage 1 has ONE more person in it than carriage 2. Carriage 2 has FOUR less people in it than carriage 3.
How many people in each carriage?

2) There are THREE carriages holding a total of 13 people. Carriage 3 has TWO more people in it than carriage 2. Carriage 2 has ONE more person in it than carriage 1.
How many people are in each carriage?

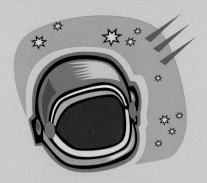

Victor has called for his spaceships to chase the train and block its path. Can you work out how many astronauts are on board the spaceship?

There are FOUR spaceships containing 28 astronauts.
Spaceship 1 contains TWO more people than Spaceship 2.
Spaceship 2 has TWICE as many astronauts as Spaceship 3.
Spaceship 3 has TWO less astronauts on board than Spaceship 4.
How many astronauts in each spaceship?

If Victor can complete the Da Vinci Challenge, the train will be stopped and all the passengers can travel home safely by spaceship!

Da Vinci Files

There are FOUR spaceships which together can take a maximum of 103 passengers.
Spaceship 1 has TWO more passengers than Spaceship 2. Spaceship 3 has TWICE as many people on board as Spaceship 1. Spaceship 4 has HALF the amount of people as Spaceship 3. How many passengers could there be in each spaceship?

Huxley's Think Tank

Estimate the size of the numbers that could fit the problem and change your answers accordingly.

Another cat-astrophe...

Time: Early morning
Place: Mrs Tiggles' house

Mrs Tiggles was very upset when she found her moggie had gone missing last Wednesday. Commissioner Crimes has agreed to help Stella find her cat and has called the Brain Academy in to assist!

REWARD

LOST CAT

Any thoughts on tracking down this phantom feline, Da Vinci?

Huxley is like a cat on hot bricks waiting to set you this Training Mission...

Mrs Tiggles and some friends are in her living room deciding what to do. Can you work out how many people are in the room?

1) $\frac{1}{4}$ of the people are sitting down. The rest are standing up.
If FOUR more people choose to sit down, $\frac{1}{2}$ of the group will be seated. How many people in the room?

2) Some more people come into the room. HALF of the people are drinking tea. The rest aren't thirsty. If FOUR more people pour a cup of tea $\frac{3}{4}$ of the group will have a drink. How many people in the room are now drinking tea?

Buster Crimes decides this is a job for the police and he calls for back-up. A team of police officers and police dogs arrive on the scene. Buster needs your help to work out how many police dogs and police dog handlers have arrived at Stella's home.

Altogether there are 8 heads and 26 feet.

1) How many dogs and police officers came to help?

It's not long before more officers and dogs arrive. Mrs Tiggles counts 26 eyes and 44 feet.

2) How many dogs are there now?

Some of the dogs and officers leave but another van load of officers and dogs soon arrive. Altogether there are 26 noses and 68 feet.

3) How many police officers and dogs are there now?

If Buster Crimes can take the Da Vinci Challenge he'll guarantee that James will be back in his basket, alive!

Da Vinci files

1) There are 72 feet altogether. What are the possible combinations of dogs and officers?
2) There are 104 feet altogether. What are the possible combinations of dogs and officers?

Huxley's Think Tank

Think about your four times table for these questions. Don't worry — all of the dogs have all of their legs!

Calculator crazy

Time: 7 pm
Place: Echo's bedroom

It's the first day of Echo's Mathematics evening class and she's already in a spot of bother. Her homework is due in tomorrow and she just can't get her calculator to work. Time to call Brain Academy!

Please save me from a detention, Da Vinci!

Huxley's Training Mission should help you with your homework!

TM

Only the numbers 1, 2, 3 and 4 are working on Echo's calculator. She can use any mathematical symbol button. Can you help Echo make a start with her homework?

1) Can you make the numbers 1 to 20 using the working keys?

2) Is there more than ONE way to make some of the numbers? Which numbers are these?

Completing these questions will mean that Echo can hand her homework in on time!

1) Investigate which numbers from 1 to 20 can be made using each of the numbers 1, 2, 3 and 4 only once and some of the operation signs?

2) Which numbers can be made in more than ONE way?

Superb! If Echo can take the Da Vinci Challenge she'll get top marks for her homework.

Da Vinci files

Investigate which numbers from 21 to 30 can be made using numbers 1, 2, 3 and 4 only once and some of the operation signs?

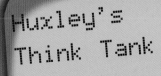

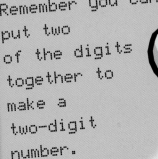

Huxley's Think Tank

Remember you can put two of the digits together to make a two-digit number.

33

Harvey's having a ball!

Time: Midday
Place: British Army headquarter

General Harvey Cods-Wallop has a meaty problem! He is planning the annual army ball for March next year and he needs to order the sausages but he can't remember how many Mrs Cods-Wallop told him to buy! The General will only be able to plan the party once his sausage problem is fixed. Prince Barrington has agreed to help.

SHOPPING LIST

- Sausages
- Balloons
- Invitation

Da Vinci, I need to save my bacon! Help!

Huxley will give you a 'grilling' with his Training Mission.

TM

Every packet of sausages contains the same amount of sausages. Can you work out how many sausages the General has bought?

1) He has FIVE full packs and FOUR individual sausages but after some unwrapping he has THREE full packs and SIXTEEN single sausages. The General hasn't lost any so how many sausages does he have?

2) He has FOUR full packs of sausages and ONE individual sausage but after some unwrapping he has THREE full packs of sausages and TEN single sausages. The General hasn't lost any so how many sausages does he have?

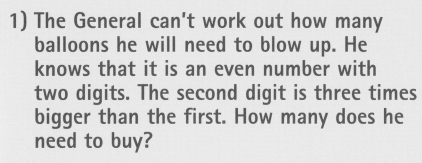

The sausages are in the freezer so it's time to start planning that ball. The General just can't seem to remember a thing! He'll need your help to get this party started!

1) The General can't work out how many balloons he will need to blow up. He knows that it is an even number with two digits. The second digit is three times bigger than the first. How many does he need to buy?

2) He needs to buy the invitations but he isn't sure how many people will fit into the British Army Headquarters' hall. The number is a two-digit square number and the difference between the digits is 7. How many invitations should he buy?

3) The General can't remember how many days after his Auntie Mavis's birthday the ball is. The number is a two-digit prime number. We know that the sum of the digits is 7 and their difference is 5. How many days after is it?

If Prince Barrington can take the Da Vinci Challenge, the ball will be the party of the century!

Da Vinci files

If Auntie Mavis's birthday was 28th April what date will the ball fall on?

Huxley's Think Tank

Always count on to the end of the month first. Then think about how many days there are in each month.

Eggs-traordinary!!

Time: Just before Easter
Place: A chocolate factory

There's only eight weeks to go before Easter and a group of D.A.F.T. agents have stolen all the chocolate Easter eggs. Buster Crimes has had a tip off that the chocolate goodies are hidden in Dr Hood's office. He's going to need to crack the security code on the door if he is to save those eggs!

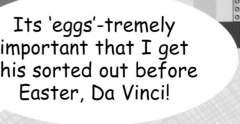

Its 'eggs'-tremely important that I get this sorted out before Easter, Da Vinci!

Huxley has a 'crack'-ing Training Mission that will stop you running around like a headless chicken!

Don't panic, you're going to need a steady hand to get through this code-breaking problem!

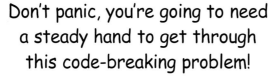

The code for the door to Dr Hood's office has FOUR digits. Buster knows that the digits are 1, 2, 3 and 4 but he isn't sure of their order. What is the maximum number of attempts that Buster will need to try in order to open the door?

M1

Buster needs to use the digits 0, 1, 2, 3, 4, 5, 6, 7, 8 and 9 to pass through several other doors in order to reach the Easter eggs. Can you help him by cracking these codes?

1) To open the first door he will need a FOUR digit number, where the first TWO digits form a number that is a multiple of 20. The last TWO digits are a multiple of 30. What is the maximum number of codes that he will need to try before the door opens?

2) To open the second door he will need a FOUR-digit number where the first TWO digits is a factor of 50 and the last pair of digits is a multiple of 40. What is the maximum number of codes that he will need to try to open the door?

3) To open the third door he will need a TWO-digit number where the first TWO digits are a multiple of 25 and the last pair of digits is a factor of 50. What is the maximum number of codes that he will need to try to open the door?

Brilliant! Completing the Da Vinci Challenge will ensure that everybody's Easter is choc-full of goodies!

Da Vinci files

1) Investigate the maximum number of attempts that Buster will need to try to crack a SIX-digit code where the first pair of digits is a multiple of SEVEN, the second pair is a multiple of 45 and the last pair is a factor of 60.

2) Investigate other 6-digit codes.

Huxley's Think Tank

A prime number has just two factors — itself and one. Be clear on the difference between a factor and a multiple. When using single digit numbers put a 0 before the digit.

Best spuddies!

Time: After breakfast
Place: Buckingham Palace

It's the Queen's birthday, but this certainly isn't a happy day for Her Majesty. She has just realised that Dr Hood has sneakily cancelled the Royal caterers who were due to prepare the food for her party.
Prince Barrington has agreed to help.

> I need to find some food and fast, Da Vinci. Can you help?

> Get the ball rolling by completing Huxley's Training Mission.

TM

> Prince Barrington has called the local Spud-2-Go. The food is cheap as chips, so as long as there's enough choice, those baked potatoes will be smashing at the party!'

How many three-course meals (starter, then main course, then dessert) can be made from this menu?

STARTERS	MAIN COURSE	DESSERT
Potato Soup	Cheesy Spud	Sponge Pudding
Potato Skins	Tuna Spud	Chocolate Cake
Potato Pate	Spud 'n' Beans	Banana Split

The Spud-2-Go waiters are busy preparing in the Royal kitchen. The Prince wants to pay them but he's having trouble working out the menu and needs your help.

1) How much does each of these items cost?
Cheesy Spud and a cup of tea costs £3.50
Sponge Pudding and a cup of tea costs £2.00
Sponge Pudding and a Cheesy Spud costs £4.50

2) How much does each of these items cost?
A tuna spud and potato soup – £7.50
A chocolate cake and potato soup – £6.00
A chocolate cake and a tuna spud – £8.50

3) How much does each of these items cost?
A spud 'n' beans and potato skins – £6.50
An orange juice and potato skins – £3.50
A spud 'n' beans and orange juice – £7.00

Completing the Da Vinci Challenge will ensure the Queen has a birthday party she'll remember for ever!

Da Vinci files

The Queen is so impressed with Spud-2-Go that she wants to give them a reward! They can receive either ONE HUNDRED potatoes a day for THREE weeks or ONE potato on the first day, TWO on the second, FOUR on the third, SEVEN on the fourth and so on for THREE weeks. What should they choose?

Huxley's Think Tank

Using a trial and error approach will help you get started. You can then change your answers accordingly!

A cracker of a 'case' for Crimes

Time: Boarding time
Place: Airways Airport

Buster Crimes certainly has got a tricky case on his hands! D.A.F.T. agents are attempting to cause holiday havoc by swapping all the luggage labels on the cases at the airports.

I want this case in the bag, Da Vinci. Where shall I start?

Huxley's Training Mission will get you off to a flying start!

Mike Ace, an extremely devious D.A.F.T. agent is causing 'bags' of trouble for the travellers. Can you use the following facts to help Buster work out how many of each type of luggage he tampered with?

1) He tampered with a total of 15 crates and rucksacks. He fiddled with a total of 30 rucksacks and cases and he meddled with a total of 25 cases and crates. How many of each did he tamper with?

2) If the total of crates and rucksacks that Mike Ace meddled with is 35, but all the other totals stay the same, how many of each type of luggage did he fiddle with?

Great, Crimes is certainly on Mike's case now! Can you help solve the problem by working out the holiday destinations of 100 troubled tourists?

America and Belgium were the destinations for a total of 50 of the tourists.

Belgium and Canada were the destinations for a total of 40 of the tourists.

Canada and America were the destinations for 60 of the tourists.

How many tourists were going to each of the destinations?

Fantastic! Completing the Da Vinci Challenge will mean that the holiday makers will find their luggage and Mike Ace and his gang will find themselves behind bars!

Da Vinci files

It took 252 minutes to sort out the luggage and the destinations.
1) If the chaos started at 11am and the flight to Belgium left at 2.08pm, did they make the flight?
2) If not, how many minutes did they miss it by?

Huxley's Think Tank

Do you think where the travellers were going makes a difference to the answers? Write down the facts you know, as soon as you uncover them!

A gem of a crime!

Time: Midnight
Place: 'Sparks and Mensa'

Buster Crimes has arrested a group of D.A.F.T. agents for breaking into the clothes store, 'Sparks and Mensa'. 'Don't nick us' begged Rob Everywhere and Nick Everything as they stuffed a pair of pants, a thermal vest and some tights down their trousers. To convict the thieves, Buster must work out which robber is holding which item. This is a job for Brain Academy.

> Da Vinci, I need your help in getting some evidence.

> Don't get your knickers in a twist, Buster – Huxley has a Training Mission to get you started.

> Right, you must bring Rob, Nick and the other FOUR D.A.F.T. agents back to the Police Station for questioning. Completing your Training Mission will ensure they are safely locked up behind bars.

1) If Buster Crimes sends TWO police vans to bring the FOUR D.A.F.T. agents back to the station, what are the possible ways that they could be divided between the TWO vans? Each van must have at least one agent.

2) What if he wanted to split them between THREE vans?

Don't forget to find all the possibilities!

M1

Can you help Buster Crimes sort out who stole what?

Between them, Rob Everywhere and Nick Everything stole a pair of pants, a pair of tights and a vest. Can you find all the possible ways that the TWO thieves could share the THREE undergarments?

Great work! Shops across the world will be safe from these villains if Buster can complete the Da Vinci Challenge.

POLICE

Da Vinci files

What if another robber, Phil Asack, was in on the act? How can THREE robbers share THREE items?

Don't forget to find all the possibilities!

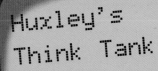

Huxley's Think Tank

Drawing a table may help you organise your thinking and find all the possiblities.

Mission Strategies 1

The TASC Problem Solving Wheel
TASC: Thinking Actively in a Social Context

Reflect
What have I learned?

Communicate
Who can I tell?

Evaluate
Did I succeed? Can I
think of another way?

Implement
Now let me do it!

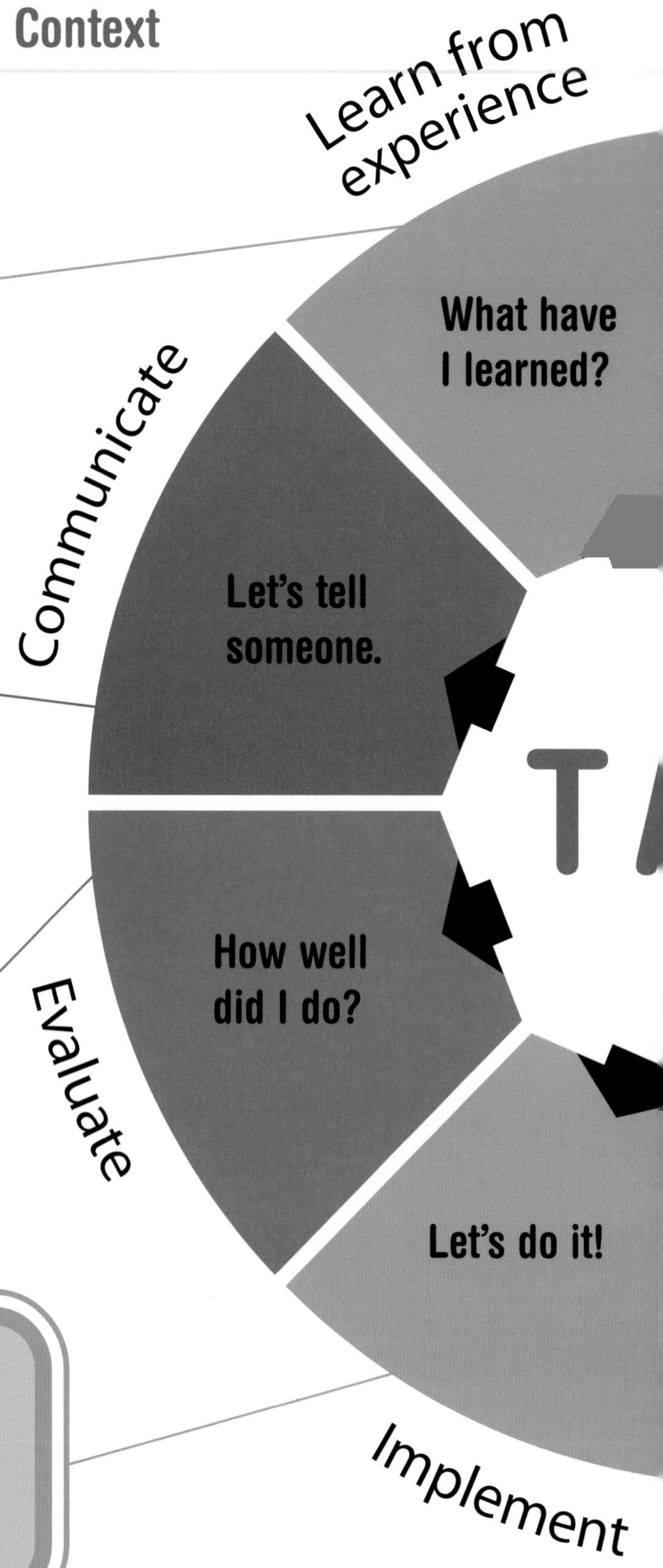

Learn from experience

Communicate

What have I learned?

Let's tell someone.

T

How well did I do?

Evaluate

Let's do it!

Implement

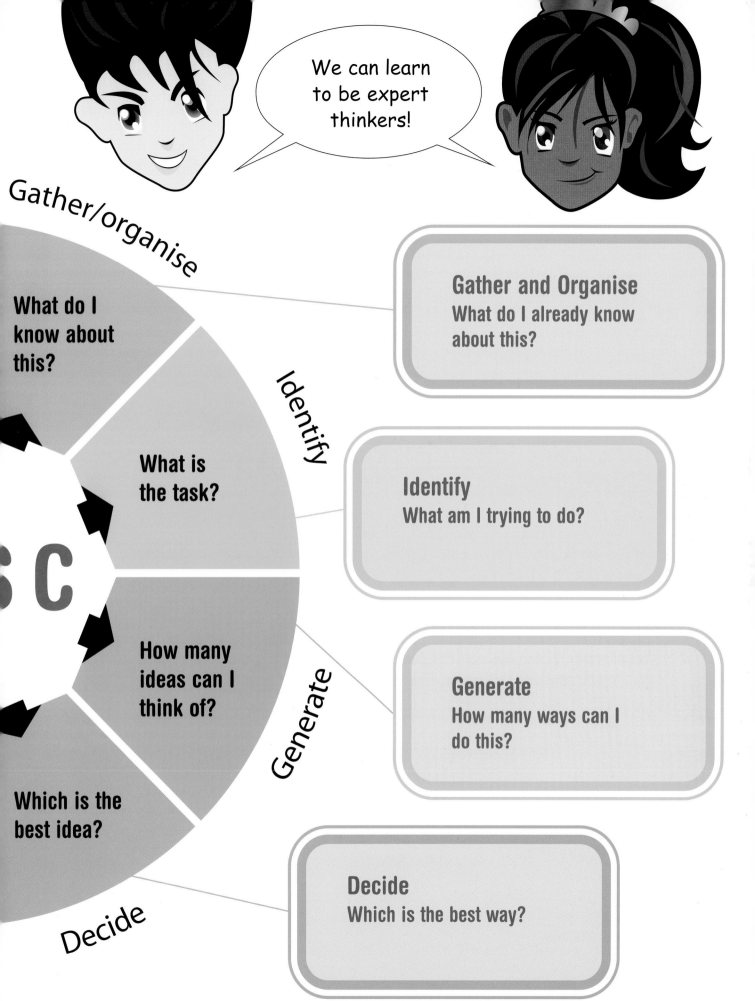

We can learn to be expert thinkers!

Gather/organise

What do I know about this?

What is the task?

Identify

SC

How many ideas can I think of?

Generate

Which is the best idea?

Decide

Gather and Organise
What do I already know about this?

Identify
What am I trying to do?

Generate
How many ways can I do this?

Decide
Which is the best way?

TASC: Thinking Actively in a Social Context © Belle Wallace 2004

45

Mission Strategies 2

MISSION FILE 3:1

These can be solved by trial and error. You could also start by saying that Apple Farm had x boots stolen and try to make a sum that totals 24 using x to represent a quantity of boots.

MISSION FILE 3:2

For the Training Mission, list all the two-digit numbers that are squares and then circle the multiples of 12. The rest of the problems can be solved in the same way.

MISSION FILE 3:3

Review your work to see whether you could find another way to answer these questions. Remember you shouldn't have any families or stamps left over!

MISSION FILE 3:4

Remember to look at the bigger picture and find larger rectangles as well. There are lots when you start to search!

MISSION FILE 3:5

When you are coming up with different combinations try to start somewhere easy – use the picture in the Training Mission as your first line!

MISSION FILE 3:6

In Mission 1 draw tables with weights down the side and the names (of cats or food) along the top. Give a tick when you know something that applies to both the top column and the weight. You should end up with just four ticks!

MISSION FILE 3:7

Mission 3:6 will help you with this one. Help Buster Crimes by using the table method.

MISSION FILE 3:8

In the Da Vinci Files start with a simple sum $(1 + 1 + 28 = 30)$ then work systematically from there.

MISSION FILE 3:9

Start your working on the last day at 0m and add the difference. Check each total at the end.

MISSION FILE 3:10
You can do these problems in two ways. The slow way is to write out all the combinations. You could also work through the number of choices each fireman has and multiply. TM1 = 2 x 2 x 2!

MISSION FILE 3:11
Work systematically through each of the different ways using a table.
In TM1 carriage 1 = carriage 2 + 1. Put this in your table.

MISSION FILE 3:12
Mission 1: Think about what facts you know: dogs have 4 legs and officers have 2 legs. You also know the number of legs in total!

MISSION FILE 3:13
There is often more than one solution to each of these questions. Use a calculator and see how many you can find. This is great practice for joining the Brain Academy!

MISSION FILE 3:14
A Prime Number can only be divided by itself and 1. Square numbers are the product of multiplying two numbers that are the same. Four is a square number (2 x 2).

MISSION FILE 3:15
First try to write the different combinations down. Do this systematically. Can you find another way to solve the problems? Clue: It has to do with multiplication.

MISSION FILE 3:16
For this Da Vinci File it might help to work with a friend. One can call out the numbers while the other adds them up. Talk about whether there is another way to solve this problem.

MISSION FILE 3:17
In the Da Vinci Files you should remember to divide by 60 to find the hours first of all. Don't forget to give you answer in minutes!

MISSION FILE 3:18
The last Mission File is the trickiest. Remember that the robbers might have no items of clothing from the robbery!

nace

What is NACE?

NACE is a charity which was set up in 1984. It is an organisation that supports the teaching of 'more-able' pupils and helps all children find out what they are good at and to do their best.

What does NACE do?

NACE helps teachers by giving them advice, books, materials and training. Many teachers, headteachers, parents and governors join NACE. Members of NACE can use a special website which gives them useful advice, ideas and materials to help children to learn.

NACE helps thousands of schools and teachers every year. It also helps teachers and children in other countries, such as America and China.

How will this book help me?

Brain Academy Maths books challenge and help you to become better at learning and a better mathematician by:
• Thinking of and testing different solutions to problems
• Making connections to what you already know
• Making mistakes and learning from them
• Working with your teacher, by yourself and with others
• Expecting you to get better and to go on to the next book
• Learning skills which you can use in other subjects and out of school

We hope that you enjoy the books!

Write to **RISING STARS** and let us know how the books helped you to learn and what you would like to see in the next books.

Rising Stars Ltd, 22 Grafton Street, London, W1S 4EX